50 THINGS TO TRY WHEN CAMPING

This book belongs to:

....

Age:...

Camping at: ....

....

Our camp!

With thanks to my parents
who made me a happy camper.
– Kim

Published by b small publishing ltd.
www.bsmall.co.uk

Text and illustrations copyright © b small publishing ltd. 2021

1 2 3 4 5   ISBN 978-1-912909-90-2

Editorial by Sam Hutchinson.
Design by Kim Hankinson. Cover design by Vicky Barker.

Printed in China by WKT Co. Ltd.

British Library Cataloguing-in-Publication Data.
A catalogue record for this book is available from the British Library.

Activities for ...
cooking, hunting, laughing,
looking, making, playing,
exploring ... **HAPPY CAMPERS!**

KIM HANKINSON

BEAR

MOUSE

FROG

HE

HOW TO
USE THIS BOOK

This book is full of daring-looking-thinking-listening activities everyone can try. Starting on any page, do as many activities as you can fit into a day and in any order you like.

The activities are colour coded to help you choose what sort you would like to do. Match the activity key below with the coloured circle in the contents list opposite or the coloured circle enclosing each page number throughout the book. There are extra pages for notes and doodles throughout the book.

Have fun and enjoy the great outdoors!

Contents checklist:

DUCK

DOG

WILD WALK

Can you spot these animal footprints? Go to page 31 for tracking tips!

Pack it in!

Pack your camping toolkit for your
wild outdoor adventuring!

MARKER
PENS

BRUSH

TORCH

FABRIC PAINT

MARSHMALLOWS

WHISTLE

OLD PILLOWCASE

WARM CLOTHES

SPRINKLES

TIMER/
WATCH

SCISSORS

CHOCOLATE-
COVERED
BISCUITS

COOKING SKEWERS

Mirror, mirror

It is hard to find a mirror when you are camping! Draw your face here so you don't forget what you look like.

Pitch in!

Help set up the perfect camp using these tips.

SEEK A SHELTERED SPOT
for your camp, avoiding exposure to sun and wind.

AVOID HAZARDS
by checking for overhanging branches or beehives.

FIND FLAT GROUND
and clear away stones and sticks.

DIG IN
using guy-lines against the wind.

COUNT AND ARRANGE
the pieces of the tent into groups to make sure everything is there before you build.

SLOT TOGETHER
the poles before connecting them to the tent.

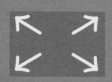

LEAVE NO TRACE
by removing rubbish when you go.

BE PRECISE
Pull out the canvas evenly with taught corners before pinning down. Make sure the outer shell doesn't touch the inside or you might get wet!

REACH HIGHER GROUND
if the area is wet!

Drive in!

Put on an outdoor movie. You will need a bright torch to cast the shadows, your hands to make shapes and the side of your tent for the screen.

BULL

DUCK

Try these animals and see what other things you can come up with.

RABBIT

SQUIRREL ON A BRANCH

Flag it!

Flags are used to mark different places.
Check out some of these flags then design
one for your own campsite.

NEPAL

This is the only national
flag that has a non-
standard shape. The
symbols represent the
Sun and the Moon.

CANADA

The maple leaf on the Canadian flag
comes from Canada's national tree.

INDIANA

There are 19 stars on the Indiana
state flag as Indiana was the
nineteenth state to enter the Union..

PAPUA NEW GUINEA

This flag features
the Southern Cross
constellation and a
bird-of-paradise, both
of which can be seen
in Papua New Guinea.

Camper's bingo

Tick off these camping sights.
Can you spot them all?

DOG

MOSQUITO

TREE

DOME TENT

BINOCULARS

UMBRELLA

BARBECUE

BELL TENT

SUNGLASSES

UNUSUAL BIRD

CARD GAME

SUNBATHER

13

Write your own camping story inspired
by the activities in this book.

DAILY DARE

Mimic the animal sounds you hear.
Will they return the call?

Flying lessons

Is it a bird? Is it a plane? Is it a boat?
No, it is you trying these tricky balances!

THE BOAT

Lie down flat, then lift your feet and chest up. Hold on to your legs and keep your back straight. Use your tummy muscles! Stop if you are straining your neck.

Try these on a soft surface like grass or sand ...

THE FLAMINGO

Stand on your left leg. Bend your right leg at the knee and reach for your right foot with your right hand. Lift your left arm up to the sky. Hold it! Now try the other side.

... in case you need a soft landing!

THE PLANE (FLYING POSE)

This is really tricky! Stand up tall. Lift one leg straight out behind you, fold forward with your chest lifted and push you arms back alongside yo Look at a fixed point to help you focus. Try on both sides.

On a beach? Up a mountain? In the forest?
Draw where are you camping.

Trailblazers

Explore the campsite using a printed map or a mobile phone. Take photos of what you see along the route and make a map like the one below.

EXIT

POOL

NICE VIEW

RVs

BEEHIVE

TALL TREES

TENTS

POND

BELL TENTS

MOUNTAIN

BEACH

ICE-CREAM

DAILY DARE

Be a night-walker! With your fellow campers, take a walk on your trailblazer route in the dark. You will discover a very different world at night!

DON'T FORGET

Plan your route in the daytime. Tie your shoelaces well and take a torch. Dress up warm – it gets chillier at night! BE QUIET! Animals are often spotted at night and noises may scare them off.

WARNING
Ask an adult for permission first!

S'more cookin'

Make and share these
super-quick 'cheat' s'mores.

You will need:

COOKING SKEWERS

CHOCOLATE-COVERED BISCUITS
Thin biscuits work best. You need two biscuits per s'more.

MARSHMALLOWS
You will need two marshmallows per s'more.

SPRINKLES
Add sprinkles if you like them!

WARNING
Hot stuff! Fire involved. Get permission
and ask an adult for help, if needed.

1. Being careful not to prick your fingers, push two marshmallows on to the sharp tip of each skewer.

2. Prepare the chocolate biscuits by arranging an even number on a plate, chocolate facing up.

3. Holding the bottom of the skewer, turn the marshmallows over the fire until they are golden.

4. Remove them from the skewer with a fork and place both on to the chocolate side of a biscuit. Place a second biscuit on top, with the chocolate layer facing down.

5. SQUISH!

6. Pour sprinkles on to a plate and roll the edges in them.

7. Wait for 30 seconds. Share, eat and enjoy!

Write about your day. It might be a good idea to save this one for a rainy day.

DAILY DARE

GO WILD! Put all the phones in an envelope somewhere safe and avoid technology for the rest of the day.

TOTALLY HANDS-FREE!

Camp compass

Use the sun to create a camp compass.

1. Use a pen to mark five big stones like this:

N (north)　S (south)　E (east)　W (west)　✛ (centre)

2. Start early in the morning and stand where you want the compass to be. Put the arrow (centre) stone between your feet. Stay here.

3. With the 'E' stone in your left hand, point towards the sun then let the stone fall to the ground.

4. With the 'W' stone in your right hand, point in the opposite direction and drop the stone.

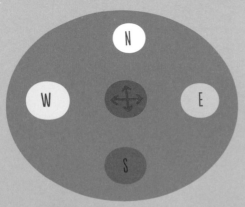

5. Drop the 'S' stone in front of you at arm's length.

6. Drop the 'N' stone the same distance behind you and line up the arrow stone.

7. Leave the stone circle and you will have a perfect compass.

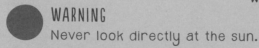

WARNING
Never look directly at the sun.

24

Draw what you had for each meal today.

Cool camping!

Discover the unusual places people camp. Can you think of any others? Where have you camped? Where would be your dream place to camp?

IN A DESERT

ON THE CLIFF SIDE!

THE CIRCUS

IN SNOWY IGLOOS

HIGH ON JUNGLE TREES

ON VOLCANOES

A slide AND a dance floor ... ? Design the ultimate camp!

Campfire tips

Learn to build a campfire. You will need an adult to help, if you want to light it.

KEEP WATCH OF THE FIRE!

OPEN AREA
Keep away from bushes, trees and overhanging branches.

SHIELD FROM WIND
A large boulder can work well.

FIREWOOD
Start small, adding larger pieces as the fire burns well.

RING OF STONES
Mark out the fire.

KINDLING
Little sticks.

TINDER
Dry leaves, bark, pine needles, paper, wood shavings.

WARNING
Never light a fire without an adult present. Check if fires are allowed where you are camping.

EXTINGUISH WHEN DONE

Knot challenge

Try these handy knots on your guy ropes.

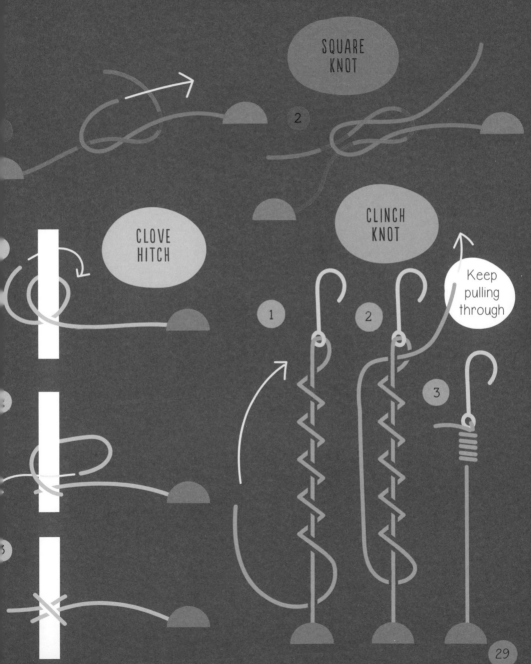

SQUARE KNOT

CLOVE HITCH

CLINCH KNOT

Keep pulling through

Campfire popcorn

No microwave to hand? Follow these tips for perfect popcorn over a campfire.

1. Use a pan with a lid. Pour in enough cooking oil to cover the base. Add three popcorn kernels and replace the lid.

2. Put the pan over the fire on a stable support such as a fixed metal grill.

3. Listen out for three pops (this should not take long) then remove the pan from the heat and place it on a heatproof surface.

4. After 20 seconds, remove the lid and scoop out the popped corn with a safe utensil. Now pour in enough kernels to cover the base in one layer.

5. Replace the lid and leave for three minutes.

6. Now put the pan back on the fire. When the popping starts, carefully adjust the lid to release the steam.

7. When there are fewer than three seconds between pops remove from the heat.

8. Add salt, or spices like cinnamon and powdered sugar for sweet!

WARNING
Ask an adult. Do not remove the lid over heat or until the popping has stopped. Use oven gloves to handle the pan.

Following footsteps

Hot on the trail, look out for these telltale signs of recent visitors to your campsite.

NEED A GUIDE?
Ask a campsite employee if there are any dangerous animals or spots to avoid. If there are, you will need a guide.

SANDY BEACHES
Animals stick to the forest edges or near to the water's edge, rather than the middle of the beach.

EARLY IN THE MORNING
Many animals like to wander at night and at dawn.

MUDDY PATCHES
Look for prints in the mud on woodland trails, riversides and under bridges.

LOCAL KNOWLEDGE
Ask about local wildlife. This will help you narrow down what you are looking at.

FORAGING FEET
Think about where animals are looking for food. That is where you will find prints.

Camping badge

Colour in these camping badges then create your own for something you did while you were camping. Have a look through this book for ideas!

DAILY DARE

Practise balancing. Try on a slack line, if you have one, or on a tree branch or log!

STAND TALL

FOCUS ON THE END

P ARMS AND
RISTS LOOSE

KEEP CHEST UP

BEND KNEES

GO SLOW AND STEADY

FEET IN LINE WITH
THE SLACK LINE

Super campers

Meet some nomads from around the world.
Can you think of any other people who move their
home from one place to another?

FIELD PALAEONTOLOGISTS

BEDOUI

RAINFOREST
EXPLORERS

WILDLIFE
PHOTOGRAPHER

MONGOLIAN
HERDERS

EVEREST
CONQUERORS!

Design a welcome sign for camp HQ.

Flash codes

Try sending and receiving secret messages
with another camper at night.

1. Turn on your torch and then
   block the beam with a book.

2. Move the book away then back again
   to flash a 'dot' on the side of the tent.

3. Then move the book
   away for a longer time
   to represent a 'dash'.

4. Keep the light covered for a
   couple of seconds between
   each 'dot' or 'dash'.

5. Use the code
   opposite to send and
   receive messages.
   Use a notepad and
   pen to jot down
   the messages you
   receive.

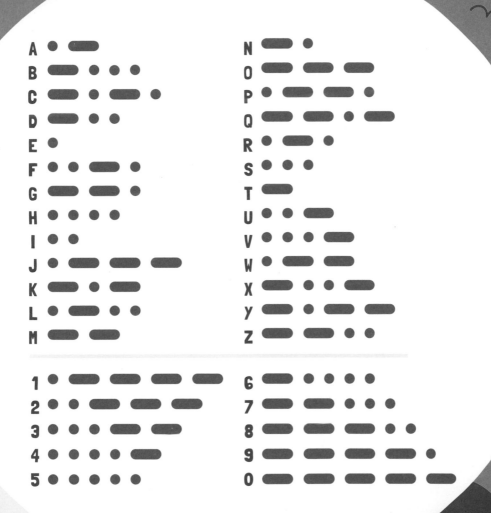

The person you are speaking to in code will need to copy this out so they can decode the flashing light messages.

Big wave!

Never lose sight of camp HQ again. Create your own flag using a stick and an old pillowcase.

1. Lay the pillowcase flat and, at the open end, cut short strips.

2. Cut templates from scrap paper to match your design from page eleven. Lay out in position. Mark what colour they will be.

3. Draw or paint around your templates in the chosen colour. Remove the paper and colour the shapes in. Allow to dry.

4. Tie a knot in every other pair of strips and then tie the flag to the stick with the remaining strips. Display your flag proudly!

Capture it!

How to play capture the flag

1. You will need two teams of at least three people each. This game is perfect for friends and family. Why not invite other campers to play?

2. Find a battleground. It should have some trees but also open space. Divide the space evenly. Each team is assigned a zone.

3. Place the flag in your zone in a fairly open area. Mark another area as the 'jail'. The other team does this too.

4. When you are ready, blow the whistle or shout 'GO!'. The aim of the game is to capture the enemy team's flag from their zone.

5. Some players stay behind as guards to protect their own flag. If you are tapped by an enemy guard, you go to their 'jail' and wait for one of your own teammates to sneak in and release you. You can go to 'jail' more than once!

6. When one team captures the other team's flag and carries it into their own zone, they have won the game.

DAILY DARE

Watch sunrise and sunset.
Can you see both in one day?
(You might need a sleep in between!)

Do not stare directly at
the sun as it can damage
your eyes.

Not very 'in tents'

Practise this morning meditation for a super-chill day.

GET COMFY

Find somewhere quiet. Sit down with crossed legs or on a cushion.
Straighten your back then move your shoulders back and down so
you feel tall not slouched. Imagine someone is pulling you up with a
piece of string attached to the crown of your head.

BREATHE

Close your eyes or relax your gaze and look down a little. Take a big,
deep breath - so big your belly goes out - then slowly empty out the
breath. Where can you feel your breath? In your nose, maybe? Pay
attention to that feeling. Breathe in and out, calmly paying attention to
the flow of the air. Now you are meditating!

DAILY DARE

Make a team for a drumming circle.
You do not even need a drum!

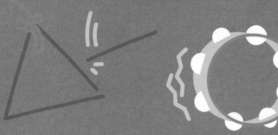 

1. Everyone finds an instrument. This can be a log to tap with sticks, hands to clap or even noises made with your mouth or body.

2. One person sets the beat. This is just a single drum beat roughly once every two seconds. It can be slower or faster as long as the rhythm stays steady.

3. The next person joins in with the first person's beat but with a different sound.

4. One at a time, each person adds their own beat or noise to go with the one before. Invite people to join in!

5. Switch the drummer order and make a whole new tune!

Draw the flora (plants) and fauna (animals) you saw today.

Pocket games

Caught in the rain? These handy games are
always with you!

THUMB WAR

Pads of fingers touching, hook your right
hand to your opponent's right hand (or left
to left), with thumbs on top. The aim of the
game is to catch the other player's thumb
with your thumb and hold it for two seconds.

TRICKERY

This instant magic show is perfect for entertaining
little brothers and sisters. With your left hand flat,
palm facing towards you, bend your index finger. Bend
the thumb on your right hand and place it on top of
the bent finger on your left hand to make a 'fake'
finger. Cover the join with your right index finger.
Then slide the right hand back and forth. It will look
like you are removing and replacing the end of the
'fake' index finger on your left hand. Spooky!

SECRET HANDSHAKE

Can you make one up with a friend and
both remember it?

Warm up and
cool down with a walk
for five minutes at the start
and end of this activity.

DAILY DARE

Go for a jog. Walk for one minute and then run for
one minute. Repeat and see how far you can go.

Base camp alphabet

Create a phonetic alphabet using words to do with your trip. Taking turns, find words that start with each letter of the alphabet. If you cannot think of anything, you are out.

A ....

B ....

C ....

D ....

E ....

F ....

G ....

H ....

I ....

J ....

K ....

L ....

M ....

N ....

O ....

P ....

Q ....

R ....

S ....

T ....

U ....

V ....

W ....

X ....

Y ....

Z ....

Dawn chorus

Wake up early and listen to birdsong and whistles. How many different birds can you hear?

Wild thing

Create a wilderness monster
and draw them on the opposite page.

Here are some
famous wild monster
ideas to inspire you.

NESSIE

Lives in Loch Ness, Scotland, and is
about 1,500 years old. Good at holding
her breath for a long time!

YETI

Lives in the Himalayas. Age
unknown but sightings reported
since 1800s! Excellent at rock
climbing and building snowmen.

SASQUATCH

Lives on the west coast of North
America. Also known as Bigfoot. Good at
playing practical jokes with footprints!

Name: ....

Age: ....

Skills: ....

Lives in: ....

DAILY DARE

Create a campfire song.
Use these rhyming words to help you!

Tent
Went
Bent
Meant

Wood
Good
Should
Could

Fire
Tyre
Higher
Wire

Sun
Fun
Won
Done

Play
Day
Hooray
Stay
May
Away

Tree
Me
Sea
See

Camp
Lamp
Stamp
Damp

Gone fishin'

Take photographs or draw pictures of these wild camping sights.

HIKING TRAIL

SOMEONE FISHING

HUT OR CABIN

TYRE SWING

HORSE RIDER

ANIMAL FOOTPRINTS

RV (RECREATIONAL VEHICLE)

Night hunters

Spot these animals in the stars.

GREAT BEAR
(Ursa major)

Watch out for shooting stars!

BIG DOG
(Canis major)

SOUTHERN HEMISPHERE

Draw all of the people in your camping party.

Good times

Make your own sundial.

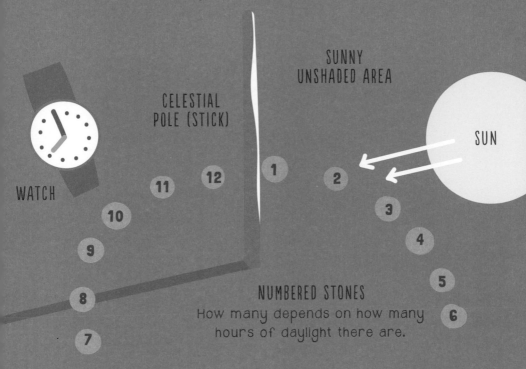

1. Choose a sunny clearing for your sundial and plant a stick (also known as a celestial pole).

2. Use a watch to tell when the time is on the hour. Look at where the stick has cast a shadow. On the shadow and close to the stick, place a stone marking the hour. In this example, it's eight o'clock.

3. On the hour, every hour that the sun is up, repeat the above step. You might need more stones, or fewer stones, depending on how many hours of daylight there are when you are camping.

4. If you start later on in the day, you can complete the clock by adding the missing hours on the following day.

DAILY DARE

Create your own spooky campfire story. Use the prompts below to get you started. Tell it to your fellow campers tonight!

THICK MISTY FOG

GNARLY OLD TREE

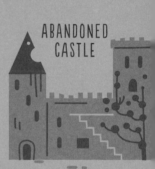
ABANDONED CASTLE

LONELY MOUNTAIN

SHADOWY FOREST

HALLOWEEN

THUNDER AND LIGHTNING

HOOTING OWL

GHOST

DARK NIGHT

FULL MOON

HEADLESS HORSEMAN

Herbivore, carnivore?

How many of these animals can you spot today. Whichever you saw more of is the winning category.

It is a good idea to check with an adult, in a book or online. Some animals might surprise you!

HERBIVORES

The vegan animals! They eat only plant-based matter.

CARNIVORES

The meat-eaters! Meat includes eating insects, fish and eggs. Scavengers such as buzzards even eat carcasses.

OMNIVORES

These versatile animals eat both plants and animals and are worth no points in this game!

Four seasons

Imagine your camp in the
different seasons. Then draw it!

SPRING

SUMMER

Autumn

Winter

Creature features

How many of these animal features can you spot?

Add a tick for each one you spot and count them up before bed!

SIX LEGS

SCALES

WINGS

TAIL

CLAWS

FIN

ANTENNAE

FEATHERS

FUR

HOOVES

HORNS

Den

Gone rogue?
Try improvising a
temporary shelter.

'Y' SHAPED SUPPORT
Look for a tree with a low
big branch or split trunk.

'Y' SHAPED STICK
Look around
for one of these
to start your den.

FRAME OR CROSS BAR
Lay between your Ys and
make sure it is stable.

LEAVES
Add last for
extra shelter
and decoration.

DOOR
You can enter here if
you have managed to
make a sturdy den!

**DRY, FLAT
GROUND**

ROOF
Lay one end of each branch or
stick on the top crossbar and
place the other end on the floor
at a bit of an angle.

WARNING
USe light sticks to make sure the shelter does not collapse.

Memories!

'It was all a dream!'
Oh no it wasn't! Draw or write one camping
memory you never <u>ever</u> want to forget.

NOTES